DON'T PANIC
SATS

AUTUMN PUBLISHING

Published in 2020
by Autumn Publishing
Cottage Farm
Sywell
NN6 0BJ
www.autumnpublishing.co.uk

0120 001
2 4 6 8 10 9 7 5 3 1
ISBN 978-1-83903-146-5

Written by Carrie Lewis
Illustrated by Katie Abey

Designed by Lee Italiano
Edited by Helen Catt

Printed and manufactured in China

Note to grown-ups

In Key Stage 1 SATs, your child will complete two maths test papers.

Paper 1 is an arithmetic test, which will contain questions covering addition, subtraction, multiplication and division. This is covered in the first part of this book (pages 4–23).

Paper 2 is a reasoning test. Practice questions for this paper are covered in the second part of this book (pages 24–43). This paper also starts with a listening test.

The pages in this workbook are set out so that you can help your child with the questions on the left-hand pages. Take the opportunity to make sure they understand the topic and explain any areas they find confusing. The questions on the right-hand pages look similar to how they will appear in the test. You can encourage your child to tackle these questions on their own, without your help, before marking their answers and discussing them together.

Parent Guide

Parents, you can use these tips and explanations to help your child understand and become confident with each subject.

Contents

Adding single numbers

Remembering your number bonds should help with adding.

Example: 5 + 5 = 10

Try filling in the blanks in these questions:

1 1 + 9 = `10`

2 8 + `2` = 10

3 6 + 4 = `10`

4 `3` + 7 = 10

Now fill in the missing numbers from these number bonds that don't add up to 10.

Example:

6
4   2

5

`9`
8   1

6

9
4   `6`

You can also do sums by counting on with a number line. Start at the first number and count onto the second number. Use your fingers if it helps. **Example:** 8 + 6 = 14

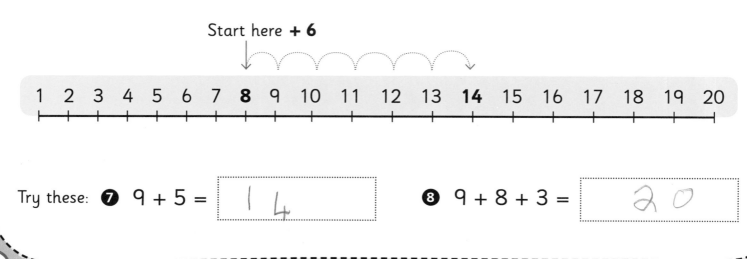

Start here **+ 6**

1 2 3 4 5 6 7 **8** 9 10 11 12 13 **14** 15 16 17 18 19 20

Try these: **7** 9 + 5 = `14`

8 9 + 8 + 3 = `20`

Answers on page 44

Practice questions

Parent Guide

SATs tests usually have only two or three questions per page, with lots of space for children to write down their working out if they want to.

1   $2 + 7 = \boxed{9}$

2   $3 + \boxed{8} = 11$

3   $9 + 1 = \boxed{10}$

More addition

Two-digit numbers are made up of tens and ones.
So **35** is **3 tens** plus **5 ones**.

We can show 35 split into tens and ones like this:

10s	**1s**
3	5

When you add a one-digit number to a two-digit number, add it to the ones side.

Example: 35 + 4 = 39

	10s	**1s**
	3	5
+		4
=	3	9

Try these:

1 12 + 5 = 2 0

	10s	**1s**
	1	2
+		5
=	1	7

2 24 + 4 = 2 8

	10s	**1s**
	2	4
+		4
=	2	8

3 72 + 23 = 95

	10s	**1s**
	7	2
+	2	3
=	9	5

You can use part of a number line to work these sums out, too. You don't need a huge number line from 0, just the part that helps with your sum. **Example:** 14 + 9

Start here **+ 9**

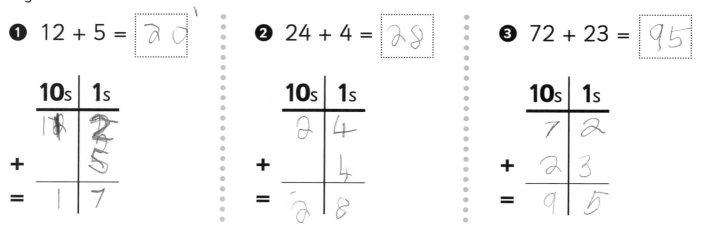

10 11 12 13 **14** 15 16 17 18 19 20 21 22 **23** 24 25

Continue the number line to get to the answer.

4 35 + 6 =

35 36 37 38 39 40

5 57 + 5 =

55 56 **57** 58 59 60

Answers on page 44

Practice questions

Parent Guide
A great way to practise this kind of sum is with money. Try to let your child play shops or use real money to buy small items.

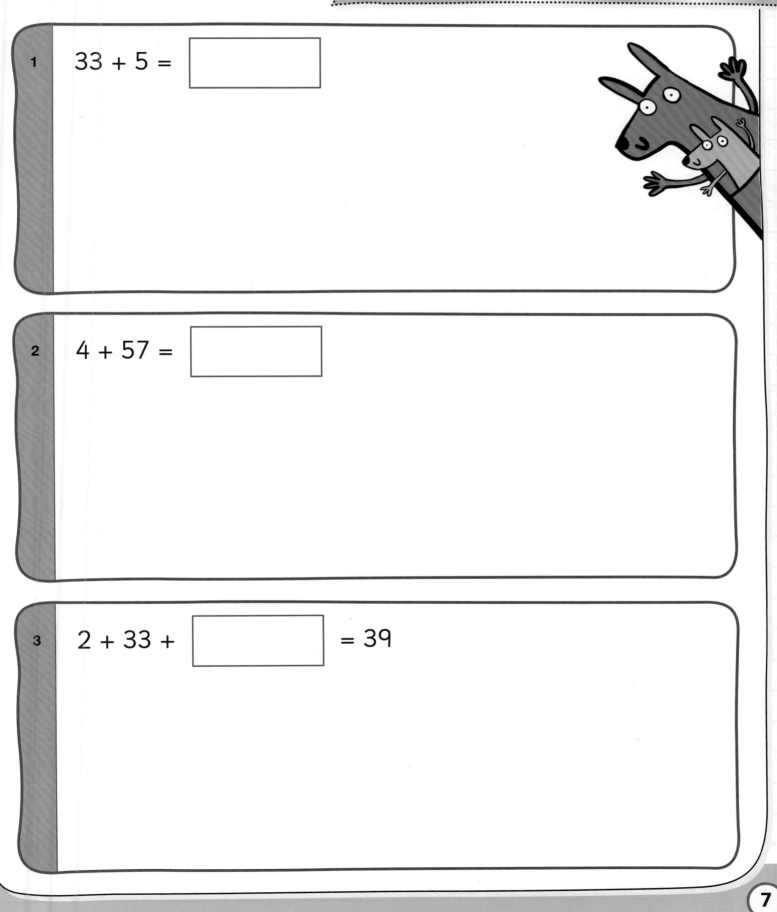

1 33 + 5 = ☐

2 4 + 57 = ☐

3 2 + 33 + ☐ = 39

Adding and subtracting 10s

When you add and subtract 10s, the 0 stays as a 0.
It's just like adding in 1s, but with a 0 after each number.

Example: 1 + 1 = 2
10 + 10 = 20

The sums are almost the same, but in the second sum, each number has a 0 after it. That's what adding in 10s looks like.

Try these: ❶ 20 + 40 = [   ]   ❷ 10 + [   ] = 60

❸ Practise counting down the tens in this number maze.
Start at 120 then count down in tens until you get to 0. Draw your path as you go.

75	8	5	90	80
20	120	132	100	70
15	0	START 120 HERE → 110	60
20	0	25	87	50
30	10	20	30	40

Now try these: ❹ 80 − 70 = [   ]   ❺ 50 − [   ] = 30

Practice questions

1   20 + 60 = [ ]

2   50 + [ ] = 70

3   100 − 90 = [ ]

Subtraction

Subtraction is when you take a smaller number away from a bigger number.
The number bonds that you learned for addition will help you with these.

Example: $8 + 2 = 10$ $\longrightarrow$ $10 - 2 = 8$ **and** $10 - 8 = 2$

Try these:

❶ $10 - 7 =$ ☐   ❷ $7 -$ ☐ $= 4$ ❸ $9 - 1 =$ ☐   ❹ $6 - 3 =$ ☐

You can use a number line to help you do subtractions. Remember to start at the highest number in your subtraction and count down the amount you are subtracting. **Example:** $8 - 3 = 5$

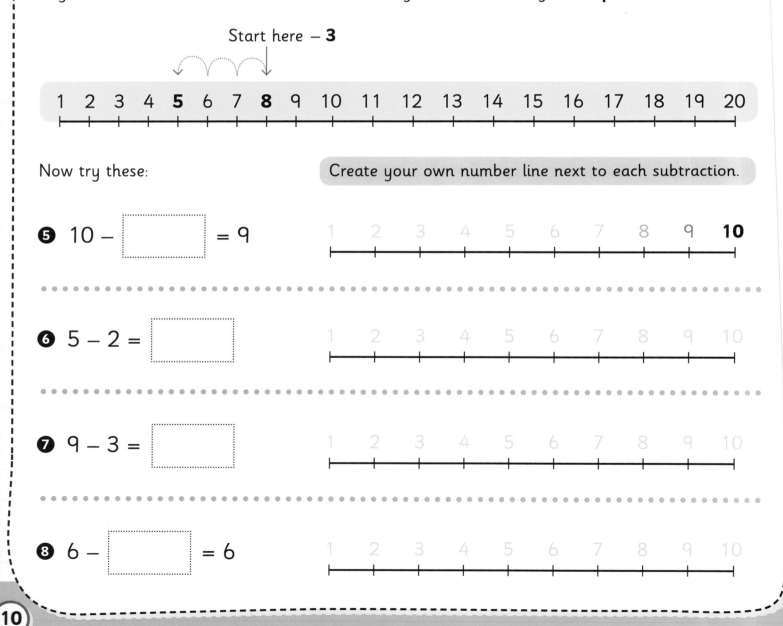

Start here – **3**

1 2 3 4 **5** 6 7 **8** 9 10 11 12 13 14 15 16 17 18 19 20

Now try these:

Create your own number line next to each subtraction.

❺ $10 -$ ☐ $= 9$

1 2 3 4 5 6 7 8 9 **10**

❻ $5 - 2 =$ ☐

1 2 3 4 5 6 7 8 9 10

❼ $9 - 3 =$ ☐

1 2 3 4 5 6 7 8 9 10

❽ $6 -$ ☐ $= 6$

1 2 3 4 5 6 7 8 9 10

Answers on page 44

Practice questions

1   9 – 6 = ⬚

2   8 – ⬚ = 4

3   6 – 5 = ⬚

More Subtraction

Parent Guide

Don't forget, there are different ways to work out these calculations. Encourage your child to use whichever method they prefer, whether that's by splitting numbers into 10s and 1s, using a number line or any other method they have been taught. Remind them they don't have to use the same method for all subtractions.

When you subtract a one-digit number from a two-digit number, make sure to subtract from the 'ones' column. **Example:** 39 – 6 = 33

	10s	**1s**
	3	9
–		6
=	3	3

Try these:

1 47 – 5 =

	10s	**1s**
–		
=		

2 29 – 9 =

	10s	**1s**
–		
=		

3 38 – 3 =

	10s	**1s**
–		
=		

You can also use number lines to help you work out these subtractions. Remember, you don't have to write a number line all the way from 0. Just write the part of the number line you need for your subtraction. **Example:** 39 – 6 = 33

Start here – **6**

25 26 27 28 29 30 31 32 **33** 34 35 36 37 38 **39** 40

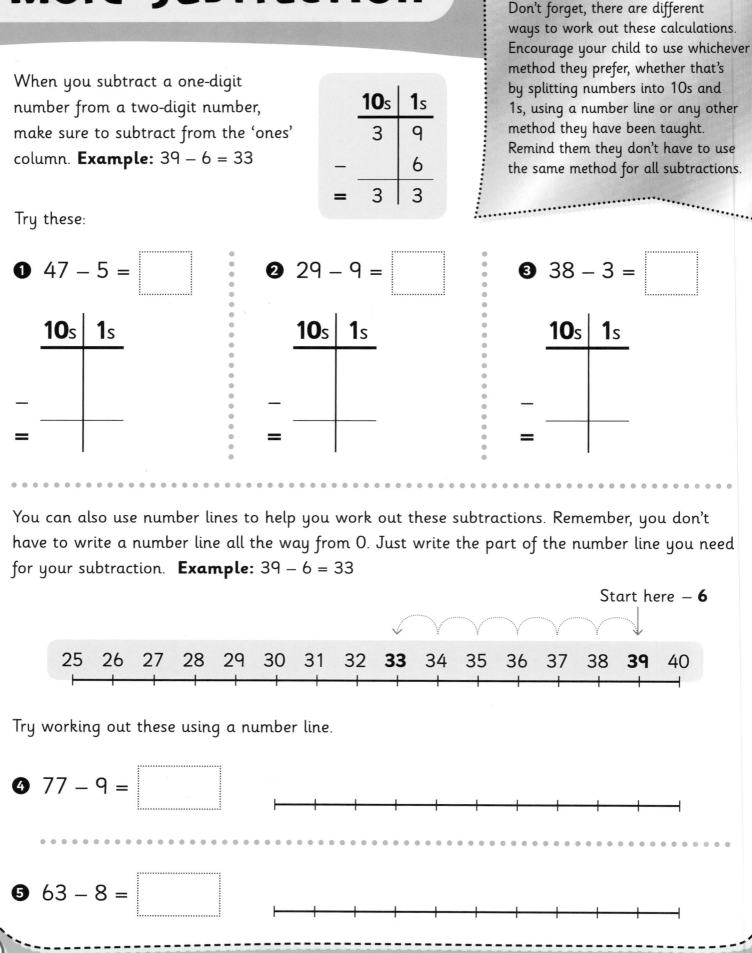

Try working out these using a number line.

4 77 – 9 =

5 63 – 8 =

Answers on page 44

Practice questions

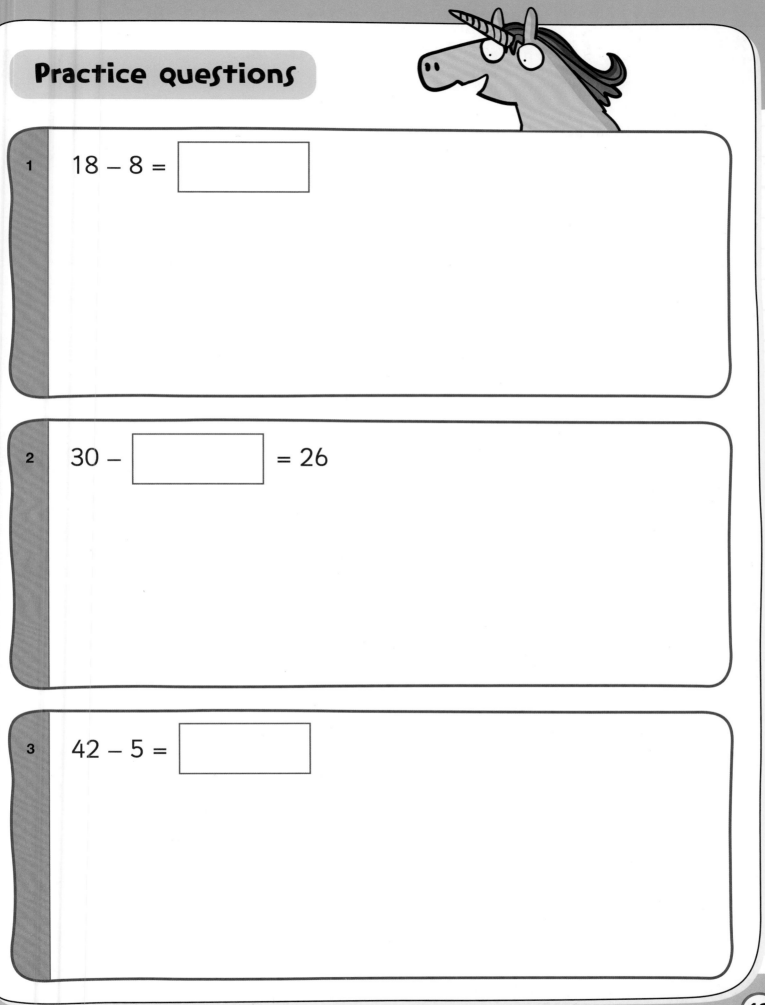

1 $18 - 8 = \boxed{}$

2 $30 - \boxed{} = 26$

3 $42 - 5 = \boxed{}$

Multiplying 10, 5 and 2

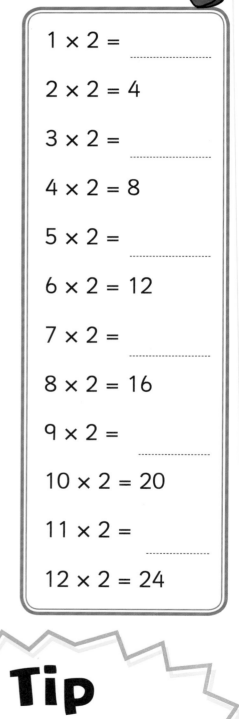

Fill in the gaps in these times tables.

1 × 10 = 10	1 × 5 =	1 × 2 =
2 × 10 =	2 × 5 = 10	2 × 2 = 4
3 × 10 = 30	3 × 5 =	3 × 2 =
4 × 10 =	4 × 5 = 20	4 × 2 = 8
5 × 10 = 50	5 × 5 =	5 × 2 =
6 × 10 =	6 × 5 = 30	6 × 2 = 12
7 × 10 = 70	7 × 5 =	7 × 2 =
8 × 10 =	8 × 5 = 40	8 × 2 = 16
9 × 10 = 90	9 × 5 =	9 × 2 =
10 × 10 =	10 × 5 = 50	10 × 2 = 20
11 × 10 = 110	11 × 5 =	11 × 2 =
12 × 10 =	12 × 5 = 60	12 × 2 = 24

Tip

A quick way to remember any number × 10 is to put a 0 on the end.

Example: 7 × 10 = 70

Tip

Any × 2 question is the same as doubling.

Example: 4 × 2 = 8

(the same as 4 + 4)

Answers on page 44

Parent Guide

Help children to remember the times tables by practising them little and often. Practising them all at once can be demanding. Two or three questions a day as you're walking to school or having a meal is enough.

1   5 × 10 =

2   3 × 2 =

3   8 × 5 =

Dividing by 10, 5 and 2

Use your times tables knowledge to complete these divisions.

Dividing by 10

1 30 ÷ 10 =

2 60 ÷ 10 =

3 90 ÷ 10 =

4 120 ÷ 10 =

Dividing by 5

5 25 ÷ 5 =

6 10 ÷ 5 =

7 45 ÷ 5 =

8 60 ÷ 5 =

Dividing by 2

9 14 ÷ 2 =

10 20 ÷ 2 =

11 12 ÷ 2 =

12 6 ÷ 2 =

Parent Guide

Help your child to see the relationship between multiplication and division. Ask questions like "If 6 × 10 = 60, then 60 ÷ 10 must equal..."

Practice questions

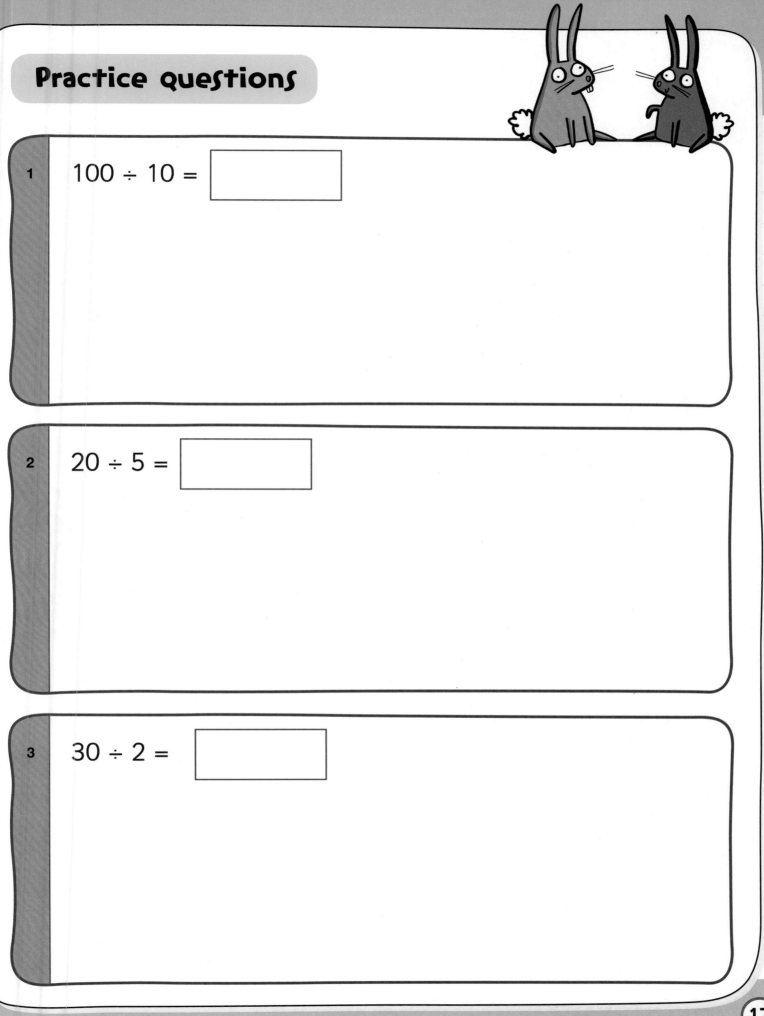

1 100 ÷ 10 = ☐

2 20 ÷ 5 = ☐

3 30 ÷ 2 = ☐

Finding half

When you split a group or number into two equal parts, you're halving it.

Draw a line to divide each group in half.

Example:

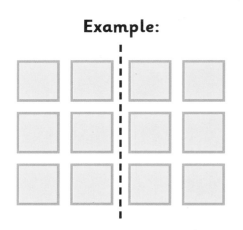

1

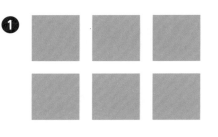

2

3

Now write half of each of these numbers in the space. **Example:** $\frac{1}{2}$ of 14 = 7

4 $\frac{1}{2}$ of 10 =

5 $\frac{1}{2}$ of 24 =

6 $\frac{1}{2}$ of 86 =

7 $\frac{1}{2}$ of 40 =

Practice questions

Parent Guide

A tip to help your children halve numbers where the number of tens and the number of ones are both even is to divide the tens and ones in half separately. E.g. to halve 48, you can find half of 4 (2) and half of 8 (4) and write the numbers side by side to get 24.

1 $\frac{1}{2}$ of 62 =

2 $\frac{1}{2}$ of 28 =

3 $\frac{1}{2}$ of 82 =

Finding one quarter

Parent Guide
When children are learning to divide shapes into four pieces, encourage them to think about dividing a pizza or cake between four people.

When you split something into four equal pieces, you're finding one quarter.

Draw lines to divide each object into four equal pieces.

1

2

3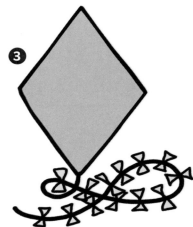

As well as shapes, you can also split groups of items into quarters.

4 Now divide the snails into four equal groups. How many are in each group?

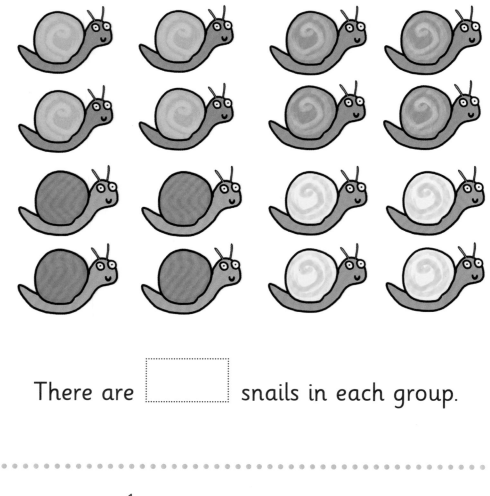

There are ☐ snails in each group.

Find a quarter of these numbers. **Example:** $\frac{1}{4}$ of 20 = 5

5 $\frac{1}{4}$ of 8 = ☐   **6** $\frac{1}{4}$ of 40 = ☐   **7** $\frac{1}{4}$ of 24 = ☐

Parent Guide

When children are learning to divide a number into four, they can divide it in half and then half again.

1   $\frac{1}{4}$ of 20 =

2   $\frac{1}{4}$ of 4 =

3   $\frac{1}{4}$ of 28 =

Bigger numbers

Using squared paper can help you with adding or subtracting bigger numbers. Colour or shade squares in rows of 10s or in 1s. You can put a cross in each square to help you count.

Example: 34 + 18 = 52

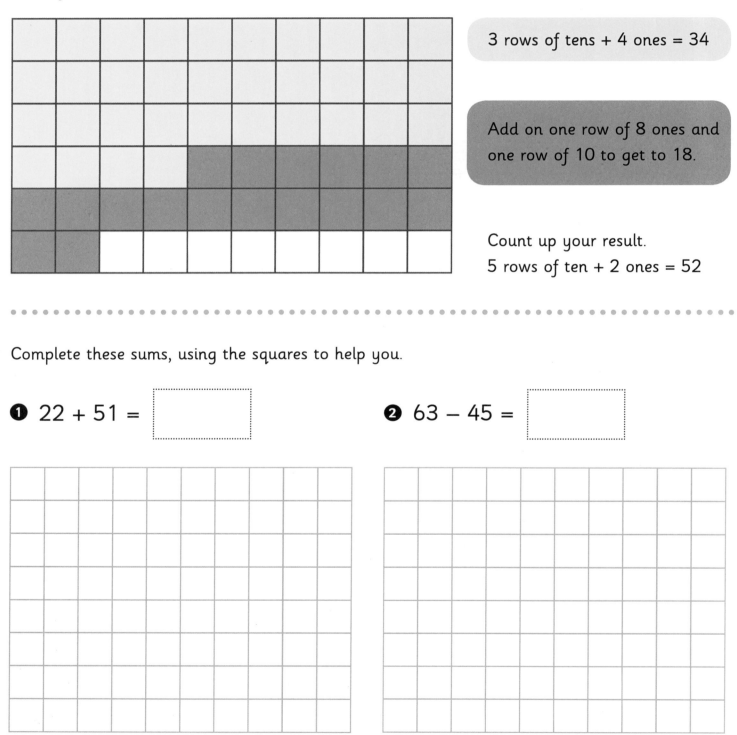

3 rows of tens + 4 ones = 34

Add on one row of 8 ones and one row of 10 to get to 18.

Count up your result.
5 rows of ten + 2 ones = 52

Complete these sums, using the squares to help you.

❶ 22 + 51 =

❷ 63 − 45 =

Answers on page 45

Practice questions

1   12 + 35 = ⬚

2   71 − 14 = ⬚

Listening

Parent Guide
Some questions in the Maths test can be asked orally. That means children will have to listen, then select answers on the paper. Practise this by reading the questions printed on page 48, while your child writes the answers here.

For the questions on this page, you will need a grown-up to help you. Ask them to read the parent guide at the top of this page and follow the instructions.

❶ 121   112   211

❷

❸ 14   8   6

❹ 62 [ ]   70

❺ [ ]

Answers on page 45

Practice questions

Parents: please follow the instructions on page 48.

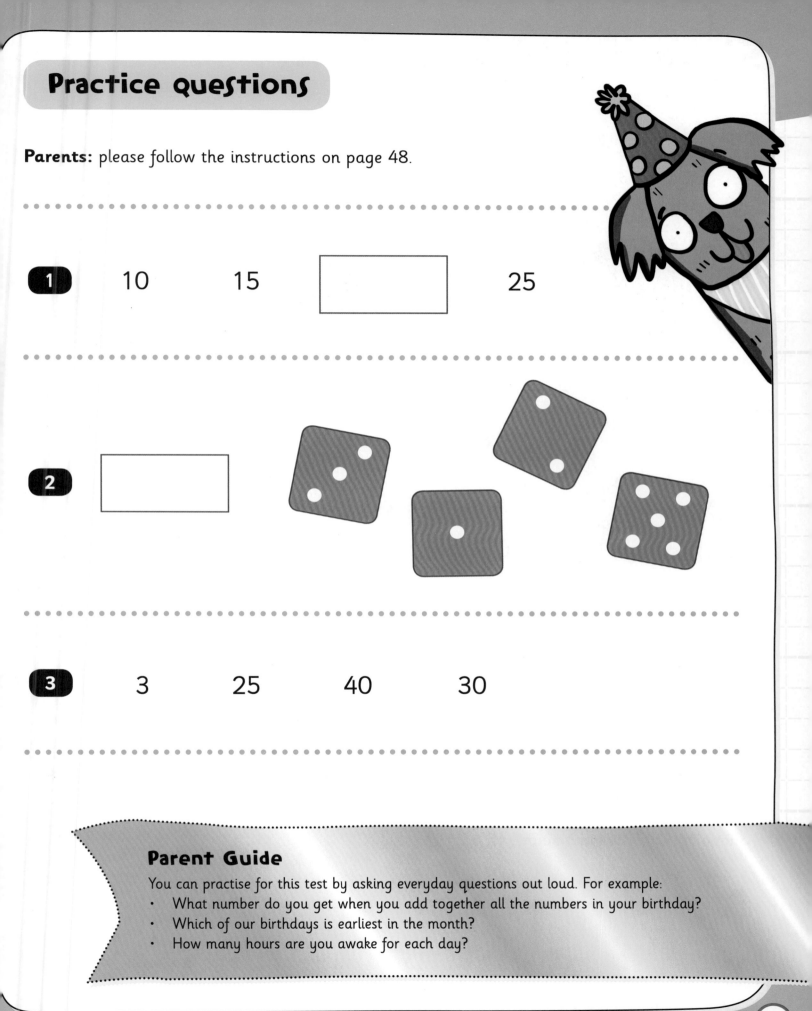

1   10   15   ☐   25

2   ☐

3   3   25   40   30

Parent Guide

You can practise for this test by asking everyday questions out loud. For example:
- What number do you get when you add together all the numbers in your birthday?
- Which of our birthdays is earliest in the month?
- How many hours are you awake for each day?

Shapes and fractions

Think of a pizza with six slices.

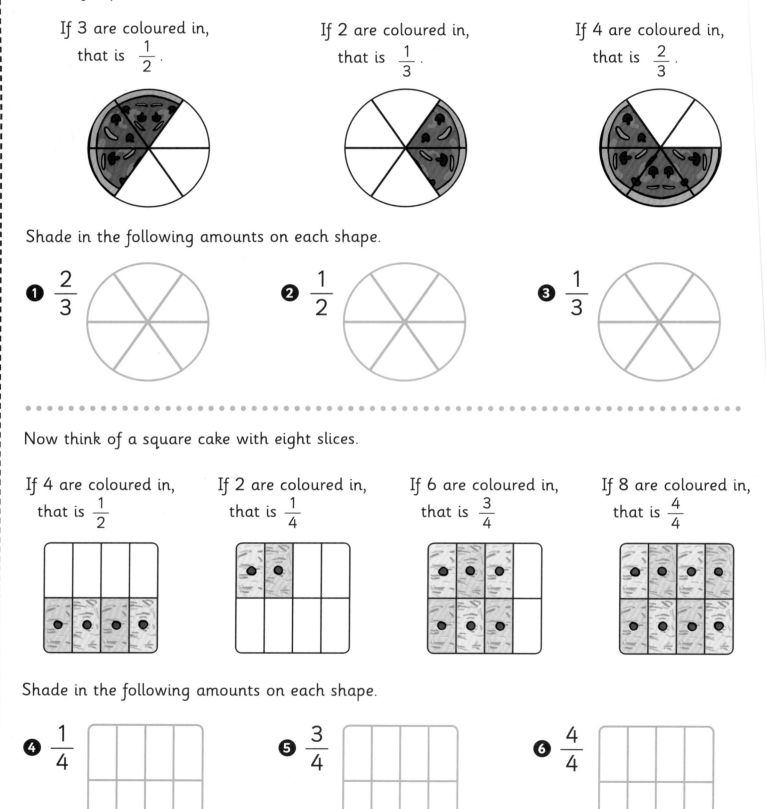

If 3 are coloured in, that is $\frac{1}{2}$.

If 2 are coloured in, that is $\frac{1}{3}$.

If 4 are coloured in, that is $\frac{2}{3}$.

Shade in the following amounts on each shape.

❶ $\frac{2}{3}$

❷ $\frac{1}{2}$

❸ $\frac{1}{3}$

Now think of a square cake with eight slices.

If 4 are coloured in, that is $\frac{1}{2}$

If 2 are coloured in, that is $\frac{1}{4}$

If 6 are coloured in, that is $\frac{3}{4}$

If 8 are coloured in, that is $\frac{4}{4}$

Shade in the following amounts on each shape.

❹ $\frac{1}{4}$

❺ $\frac{3}{4}$

❻ $\frac{4}{4}$

Practice questions

Circle the correct shape in each question.

1 $\frac{1}{3}$ shaded

2 $\frac{1}{2}$ shaded

3 $\frac{4}{4}$ shaded

Parent Guide

Remind children that shapes can be divided in different ways, e.g. wedges, slices and squares. Children need to count the number of sections in each shape to know the answer.

Shapes

Different shapes have different numbers of sides and vertices (corners).
Some shapes, like squares and rectangles, have vertices that are a right angle.

1 Copy the labels to match the correct parts of the shape.

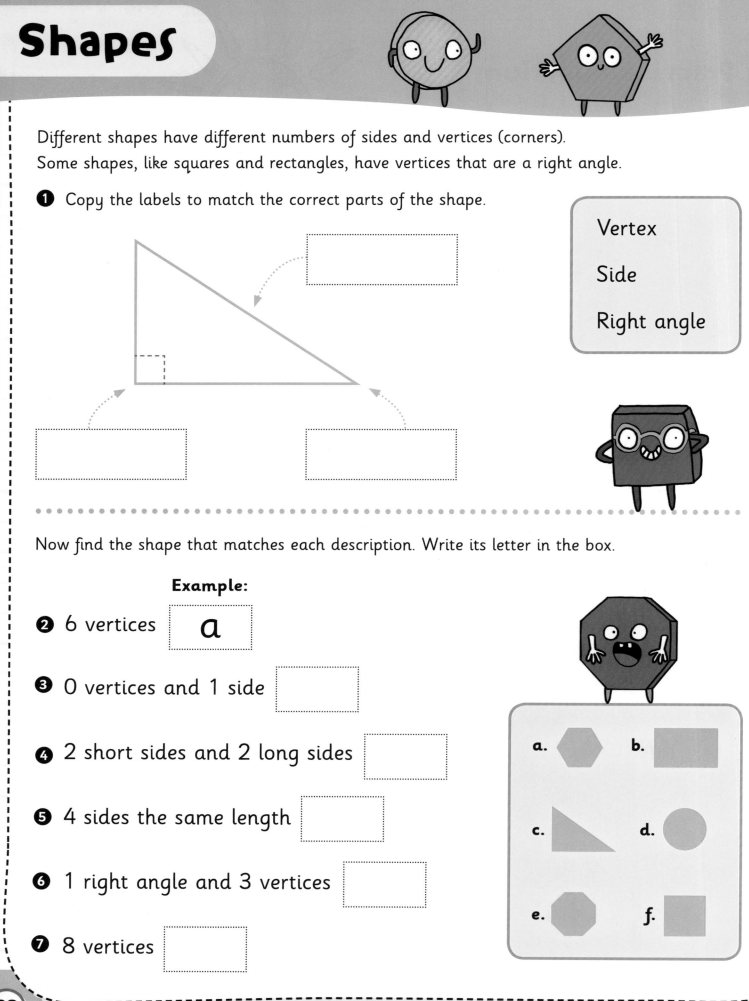

Vertex

Side

Right angle

Now find the shape that matches each description. Write its letter in the box.

Example:

2 6 vertices a

3 0 vertices and 1 side

4 2 short sides and 2 long sides

5 4 sides the same length

6 1 right angle and 3 vertices

7 8 vertices

a.   b.

c.   d.

e.   f.

Practice questions

1 Match each description with the correct shape.
One has been done for you.

3 vertices and 3 sides   circle

1 side and no right-angles   hexagon

6 vertices and 6 sides   square

4 equal sides   triangle

2 Draw a tick ✓ by the right angle.

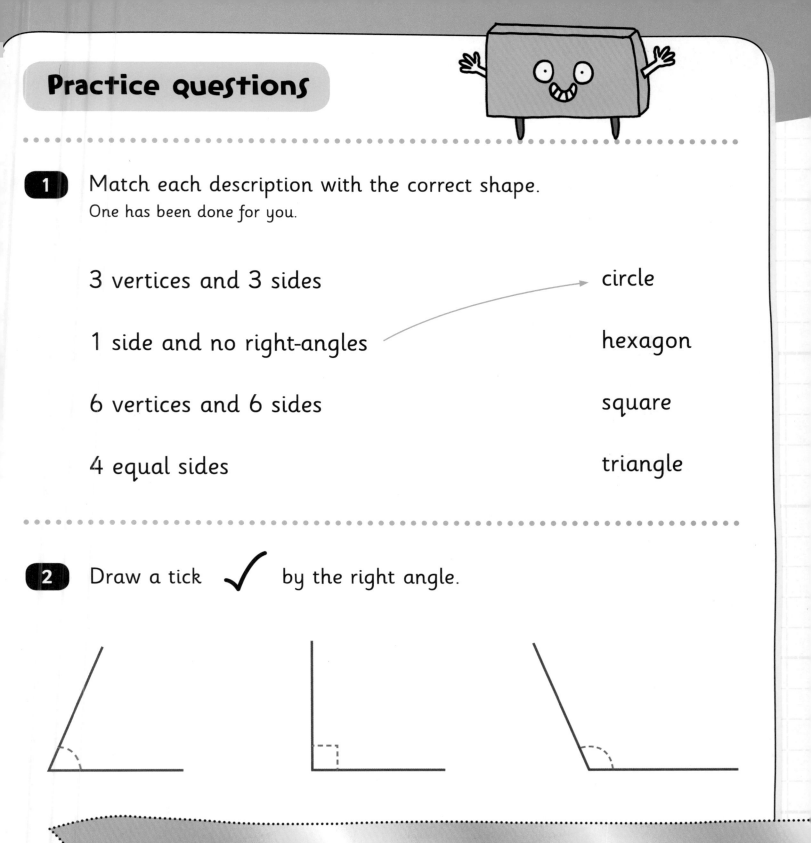

Parent Guide

Encourage your child to spot different shapes in their daily life and ask them to describe how many sides, vertices and right angles they can count in the shapes they find. Ask them how many triangles they can spot in a room or make a game by saying they can score different points for every shape they spot over the course of an afternoon: 1 point for a circle, 3 points for a triangle, 4 points for a square, 6 points for a hexagon and so on. See who can get the highest score.

Words for Size

Words like tall, short, long, big and small can all tell you about the size of an object.

Try these size problems.

1 Read the text, then look at the picture and write the children's names in the right spaces.

> Martha is taller than Owen, but shorter than Kai.
> Owen is taller than Heena.

| | | **Owen** | |

2 Number the umbrellas from 1–5, with 1 as the biggest and 5 as the smallest.

Practice questions

1 Put the four pencils in order from tallest to shortest.
One has been done for you.

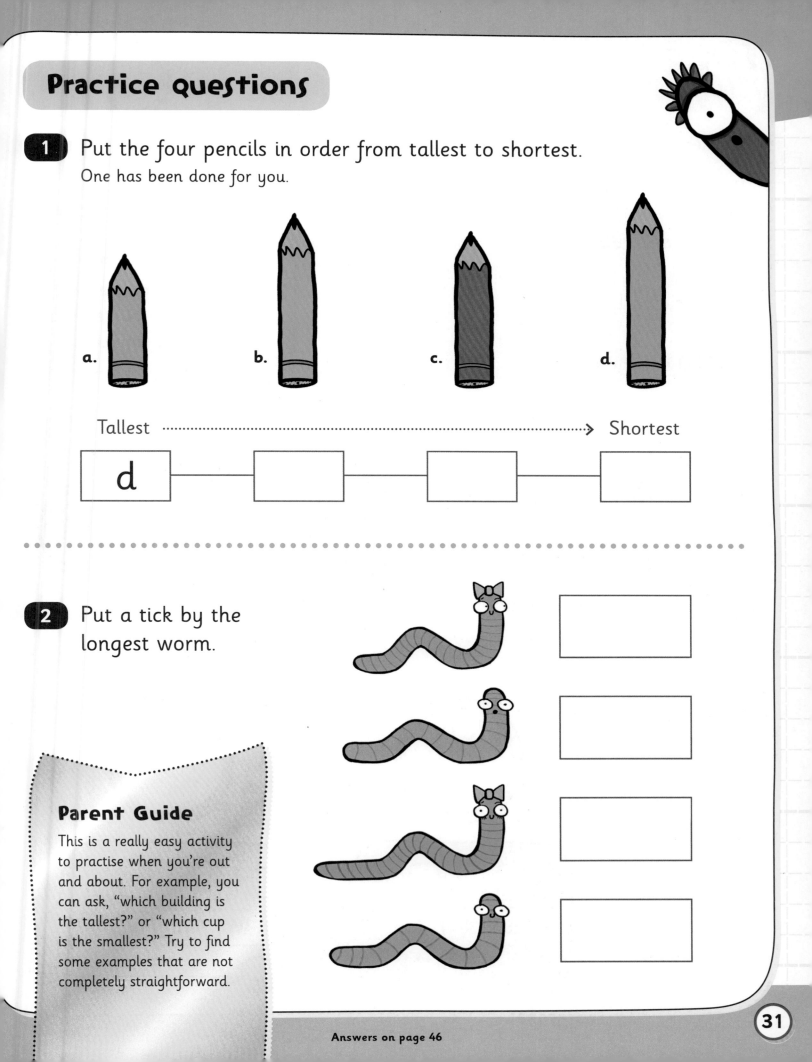

a.   b.   c.   d.

Tallest ···➔ Shortest

d			

2 Put a tick by the longest worm.

Parent Guide

This is a really easy activity to practise when you're out and about. For example, you can ask, "which building is the tallest?" or "which cup is the smallest?" Try to find some examples that are not completely straightforward.

Answers on page 46

Time

We measure time in seconds, minutes and hours.

Write these times as minutes and seconds. One has been done for you.

100 seconds = | 1 minute and 40 seconds |

❶ 70 seconds = | |

❷ 110 seconds = | |

Tip

Remember:
there are 60 seconds
in a minute.

Now try to solve these..

❸ Ed wanted to see how long it would take him to run around his house. He timed himself three times.

Which run was the fastest?

Tick the correct stopwatch.

❹ Vic needs to take the bus to his uncle's house. Both buses take 1 hour to get there.

Which bus will arrive first?

Bus | |

a

b

LEAVES 10:30

LEAVES 10:45

Practice questions

1 Which bus should you get to arrive in Smileton at 11 o'clock?
Tick the correct bus.

	LEAVES GRINFORD	ARRIVES AT SMILETON
Bus A	8:30	9:30
Bus B	9:00	10:00
Bus C	9:30	10:30
Bus D	10:00	11:00

2 Who completed the sack race in the fastest time?
Write the name in the box.

Sally   40 seconds

Hanna   1 minute

Finn   55 seconds

Alec   1 minute 5 seconds

Answers on page 46

Money

Money can be split into pounds (£) and pennies (p).

1 Can you remember how many pennies make £1?
Circle your answer.

60   100   50

Now look at these coins. There are lots of ways of making £1 from them.

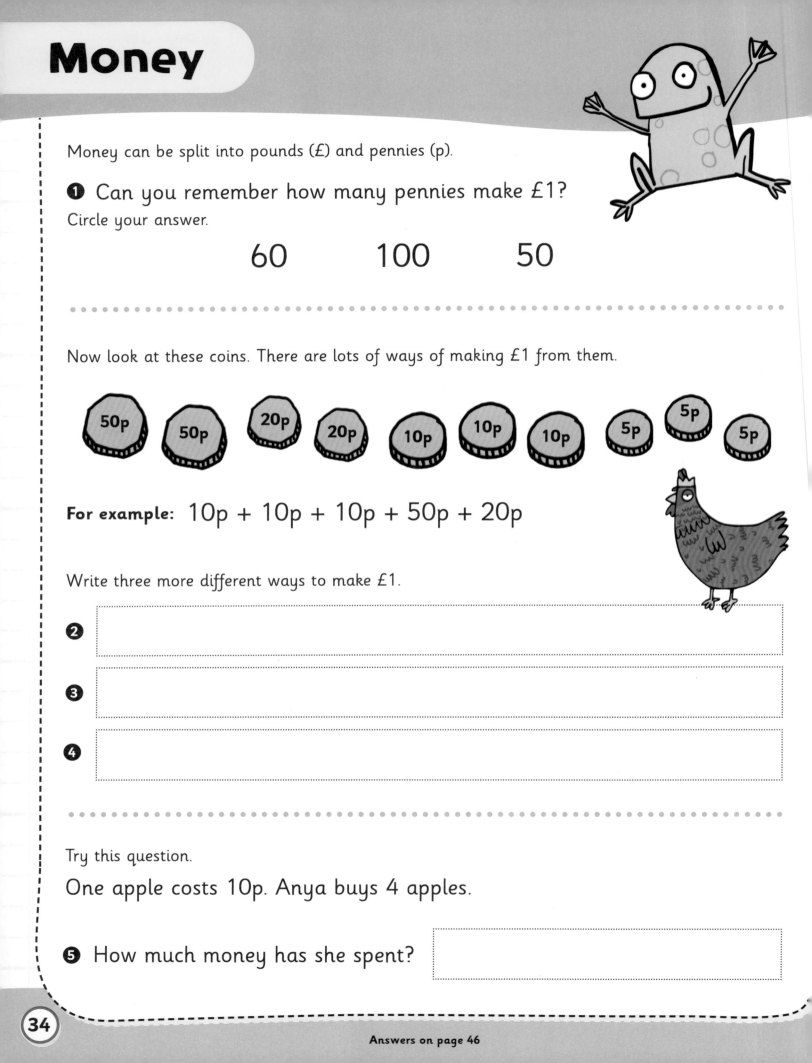

For example: 10p + 10p + 10p + 50p + 20p

Write three more different ways to make £1.

2

3

4

Try this question.

One apple costs 10p. Anya buys 4 apples.

5 How much money has she spent?

Answers on page 46

Practice questions

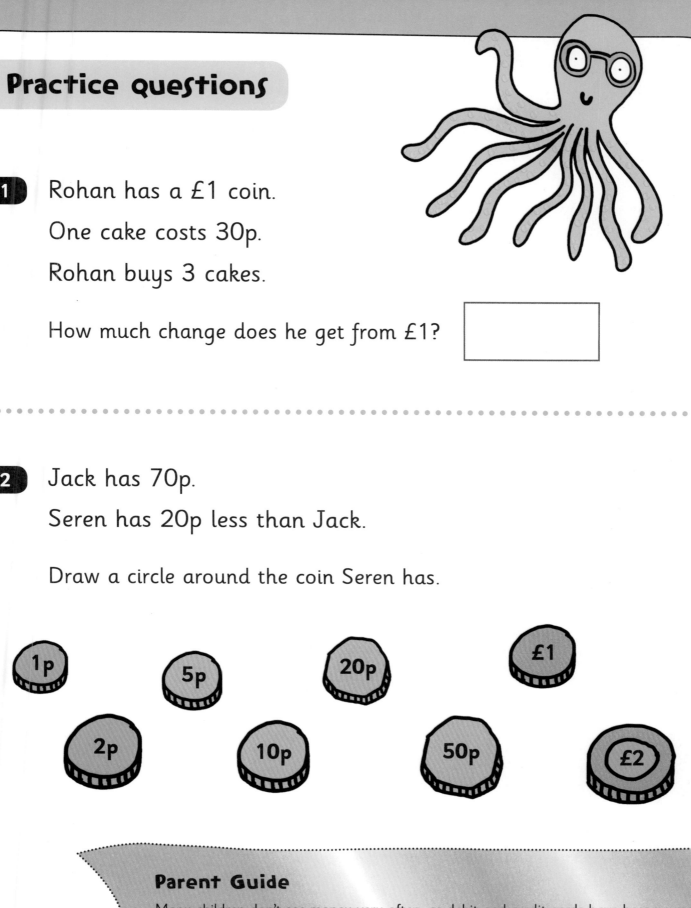

1 Rohan has a £1 coin.

One cake costs 30p.

Rohan buys 3 cakes.

How much change does he get from £1?

2 Jack has 70p.

Seren has 20p less than Jack.

Draw a circle around the coin Seren has.

1p

5p

20p

£1

2p

10p

50p

£2

Parent Guide

Many children don't see money very often, as debit and credit cards have become more common. If possible, let children use small amounts of change to buy things in real shops. This helps them to understand what adding money is really all about.

Sequences

Sequences are patterns. If you look at the pattern carefully,
you can work out what comes next in the sequence.

Which shape comes next? Draw it.

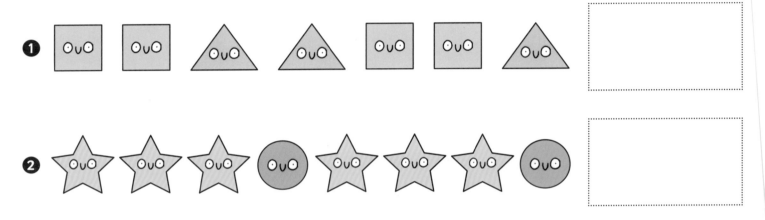

1

2

When you are solving a number sequence, look at the difference between the
numbers to work out which one comes next.

Example: 2   4   6 . . .

First, work out the difference between 2 and 4, then the difference between 4 and 6.

3 Can you use that to work out the next number?

Write the number on the next bead in each sequence.

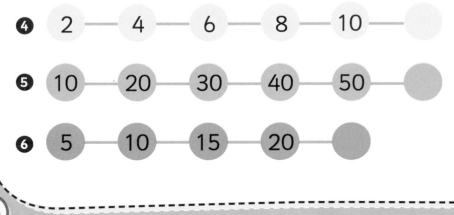

4 2 — 4 — 6 — 8 — 10 —

5 10 — 20 — 30 — 40 — 50 —

6 5 — 10 — 15 — 20 —

Answers on page 47

1 Nayan has made number patterns with his cars.

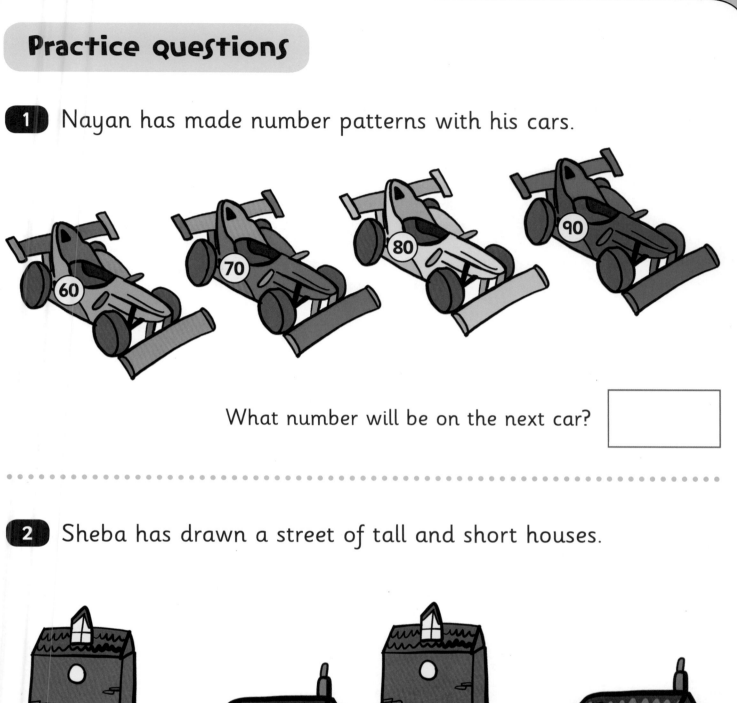

What number will be on the next car?

2 Sheba has drawn a street of tall and short houses.

What number will be on the next short house?

Symbols

Sometimes it can be easy to get maths symbols muddled up. Try to remember what each symbol does and remember to look at the symbol really carefully when you are working things out.

❶ Draw lines to match each symbol to its name.

Add   Take away   Divide   Times

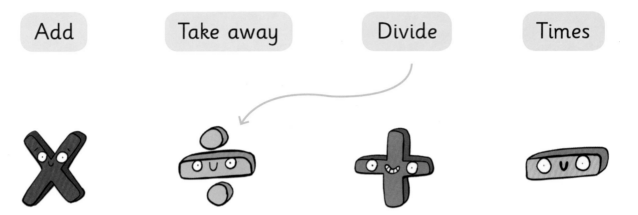

Which card will make each number sentence correct?

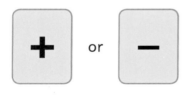

❷ 3 ☐ 12 = 15

❸ 15 ☐ 11 = 4

❹ 43 ☐ 20 = 63

❺ 60 + 20 ☐ 4 = 76

Now work out which card will complete these number sentences.

❻ 5 ☐ 10 = 50

❼ 2 ☐ 3 = 6

❽ 70 ☐ 10 = 7

❾ 10 ☐ 2 = 20

Answers on page 47

Choose the correct symbol card to make each number sentence correct.

1 14 ☐ 2 = 7

2 5 ☐ 2 = 10

3 40 ☐ 2 = 20

4 40 ☐ 2 = 38

Word problems

A top tip with word problems is to read everything before answering anything!
Read carefully and then think carefully, too, before writing anything down.

Try these.

❶ There are 40 apples and 4 bags to put them in.
Help Kim work out how many apples must go in each bag so that none are left over.

Choose the best symbol to complete the sum and write the answer.

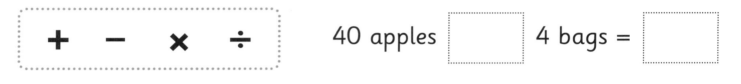

+ − ✕ ÷   40 apples [ ]   4 bags = [ ]

❷ Stefan has 45p made up of these coins.

Fatima has 60p.
Write or draw some coins to make 60p.

❸ Krit snapped his ruler. It was a 30cm ruler. 13cm have snapped off.

How long is Krit's ruler now? [ ]

Parent Guide

Word problems in the SATs tests are designed to test children's thinking skills. They can be about different topics and areas of maths. Children need to pay attention to the details and work the answer out logically. You can help to prepare for this by showing questions in lots of different formats, not always in numbers.

For example: you have six pairs of shoes. How many shoes have you got all together?

Answers on page 47

Practice questions

1 There are 24 children in class 2C.
2 children sit at each table.
There are 10 tables.

How many more tables do they need?

[ ]

2 Malik measures the temperature of 2 cups of water.
Cup A is 28 °C.
Cup B is 5 degrees warmer.

Draw the correct temperature on the thermometer.

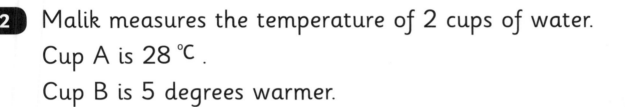

Symmetry

A line of symmetry is the line that goes down the middle of something so that both sides are exactly the same.

Some shapes, like these, have 1 line of symmetry.

Draw the line of symmetry on these shapes. One has been done for you.

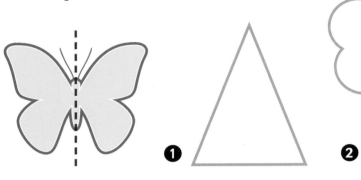

Other shapes, like these, have 2 or more lines of symmetry.
How many lines can you draw on each shape?

How many lines of symmetry does each of these shapes have?
Write your answer in the boxes below.

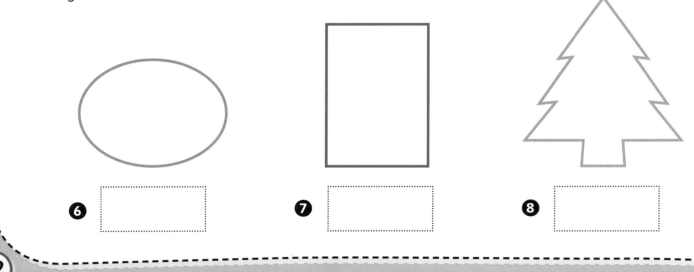

Answers on page 47

Practice questions

1 Draw two lines of symmetry on this shape.

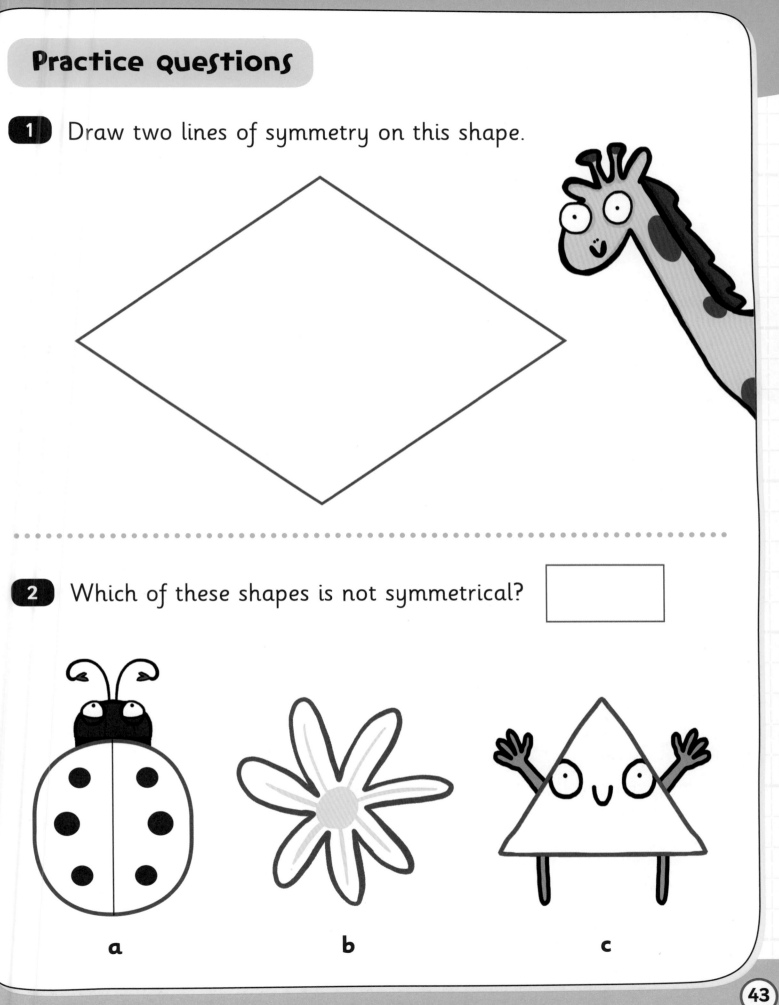

2 Which of these shapes is not symmetrical?

a

b

c

Answers

Pages 4–5: Adding single numbers

1. 1 + 9 = 10
2. 8 + 2 = 10
3. 6 + 4 = 10
4. 3 + 7 = 10

5.

9

8	1

6.

9

4	**5**

7. 9 + 5 = 14
8. 9 + 8 + 3 = 20

Practice questions

1. 2 + 7 = 9
2. 3 + 8 = 11
3. 9 + 1 = 10

Pages 6–7: More addition

1. 12 + 5 = 17
2. 24 + 4 = 28
3. 72 + 23 = 95
4. 35 + 6 = 41
5. 57 + 5 = 62

Practice questions

1. 33 + 5 = 38
2. 4 + 57 = 61
3. 2 + 33 + 4 = 39

Pages 8–9: Adding and subtracting 10s

1. 20 + 40 = 60
2. 10 + 50 = 60
3.

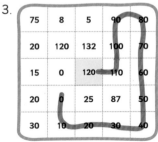

4. 80 – 70 = 10
5. 50 – 20 = 30

Practice questions

1. 20 + 60 = 80
2. 50 + 20 = 70
3. 100 – 90 = 10

Pages 10–11: Subtraction

1. 10 – 7 = 3
2. 7 – 3 = 4
3. 9 – 1 = 8
4. 6 – 3 = 3
5. 10 – 1 = 9
6. 5 – 2 = 3
7. 9 – 3 = 6
8. 6 – 0 = 6

Practice questions

1. 9 – 6 = 3
2. 8 – 4 = 4
3. 6 – 5 = 1

Pages 12–13: More subtraction

1. 47 – 5 = 42
2. 29 – 9 = 20
3. 38 – 3 = 35
4. 77 – 9 = 68
5. 63 – 8 = 55

Practice questions

1. 18 – 8 = 10
2. 30 – 4 = 26
3. 42 – 5 = 37

Pages 14–15: Multiplying 10s, 5s and 2s

1 × 10 = 10	1 × 5 = **5**	1 × 2 = **2**
2 × 10 = **20**	2 × 5 = 10	2 × 2 = 4
3 × 10 = 30	3 × 5 = **15**	3 × 2 = **6**
4 × 10 = **40**	4 × 5 = 20	4 × 2 = 8
5 × 10 = 50	5 × 5 = **25**	5 × 2 = **10**
6 × 10 = **60**	6 × 5 = 30	6 × 2 = 12
7 × 10 = 70	7 × 5 = **35**	7 × 2 = **14**
8 × 10 = **80**	8 × 5 = 40	8 × 2 = 16
9 × 10 = 90	9 × 5 = **45**	9 × 2 = **18**
10 × 10 = **100**	10 × 5 = 50	10 × 2 = 20
11 × 10 = 110	11 × 5 = **55**	11 × 2 = **22**
12 × 10 = **120**	12 × 5 = 60	12 × 2 = 24

Practice questions

1. 5 × 10 = 50
2. 3 × 2 = 6
3. 8 × 5 = 40

Pages 16–17: Dividing by 10, 5 and 2

1. $30 \div 10 = 3$
2. $60 \div 10 = 6$
3. $90 \div 10 = 9$
4. $120 \div 10 = 12$
5. $25 \div 5 = 5$
6. $10 \div 5 = 2$
7. $45 \div 5 = 9$
8. $60 \div 5 = 12$
9. $14 \div 2 = 7$
10. $20 \div 2 = 10$
11. $12 \div 2 = 6$
12. $6 \div 2 = 3$

Practice questions

1. $100 \div 10 = 10$
2. $20 \div 5 = 4$
3. $30 \div 2 = 15$

Pages 18–19: Finding half

1.

2.

3.

4. $\frac{1}{2}$ of $10 = 5$
5. $\frac{1}{2}$ of $24 = 12$
6. $\frac{1}{2}$ of $86 = 43$
7. $\frac{1}{2}$ of $40 = 20$

Practice questions

1. $\frac{1}{2}$ of $62 = 31$
2. $\frac{1}{2}$ of $28 = 14$
3. $\frac{1}{2}$ of $82 = 41$

Pages 20–21: Finding one quarter

1. 2.

3.

4. There are 4 snails in each group.
5. $\frac{1}{4}$ of $8 = 2$
6. $\frac{1}{4}$ of $40 = 10$
7. $\frac{1}{4}$ of $24 = 6$

Practice questions

1. $\frac{1}{4}$ of $20 = 5$
2. $\frac{1}{4}$ of $4 = 1$
3. $\frac{1}{4}$ of $28 = 7$

Pages 22–23: Bigger numbers

1. $22 + 51 = 73$
2. $63 - 45 = 18$

Practice questions

1. $12 + 35 = 47$
2. $71 - 14 = 57$

Pages 24–25: Listening

1. 211
2.

3. 6
4. 66
5. 8 wheels

Practice questions

1. 20
2. 11
3. 30

Answers

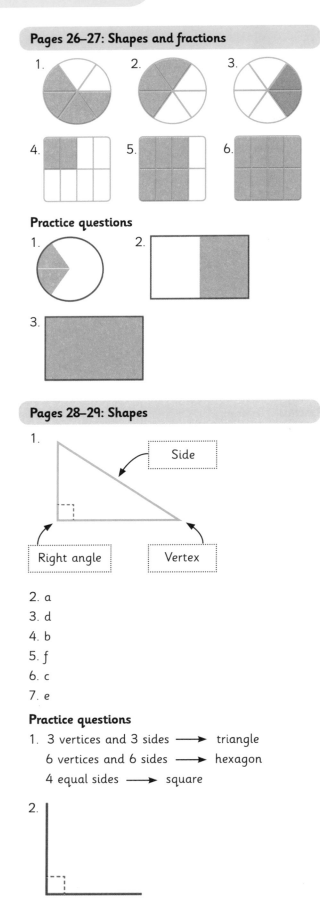

Pages 26–27: Shapes and fractions

Practice questions

Pages 28–29: Shapes

1.
Side
Right angle
Vertex

2. a
3. d
4. b
5. f
6. c
7. e

Practice questions

1. 3 vertices and 3 sides ⟶ triangle
   6 vertices and 6 sides ⟶ hexagon
   4 equal sides ⟶ square

2.

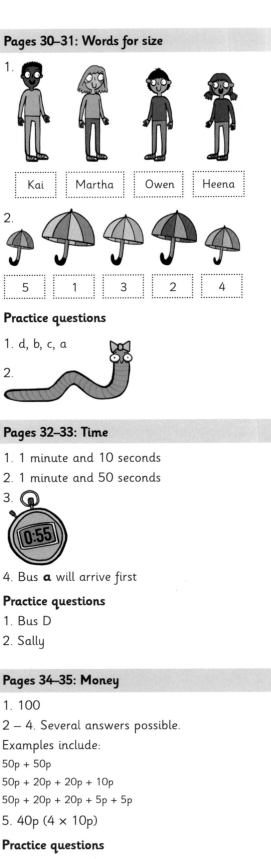

Pages 30–31: Words for size

1. Kai   Martha   Owen   Heena

2. 5   1   3   2   4

Practice questions

1. d, b, c, a

2.

Pages 32–33: Time

1. 1 minute and 10 seconds
2. 1 minute and 50 seconds
3. 0:55

4. Bus **a** will arrive first

Practice questions

1. Bus D
2. Sally

Pages 34–35: Money

1. 100
2 – 4. Several answers possible.
Examples include:
50p + 50p
50p + 20p + 20p + 10p
50p + 20p + 20p + 5p + 5p
5. 40p (4 × 10p)

Practice questions

1. 10p

2. 50p

Pages 36–37: Sequences

1.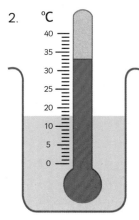

2.

3. 8
4. 12
5. 60
6. 25

Practice questions

1. 100
2. 14

Pages 38–39: Symbols

1. Add   Take away   Divide   Times

2. 3 + 12 = 15
3. 15 − 11 = 4
4. 43 + 20 = 63
5. 60 + 20 − 4 = 76
6. 5 × 10 = 50
7. 2 × 3 = 6
8. 70 ÷ 10 = 7
9. 10 × 2 = 20

Practice questions

1. 14 ÷ 2 = 7
2. 5 × 2 = 10
3. 40 ÷ 2 = 20
4. 40 − 2 = 38

Pages 40–41: Word problems

1. 40 apples ÷ 4 bags = 10 apples
2. Several answers possible. Examples include:
50p + 10p
20p + 20p + 20p
20p + 20p + 10p + 10p
3. 30cm − 13 cm = 17cm

Practice questions

1. 2 tables

2.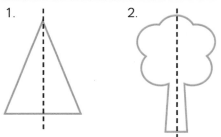

Pages 42–43: Symmetry

1. 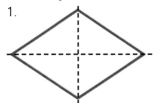   2.

3. Circles have infinite lines of symmetry

4. 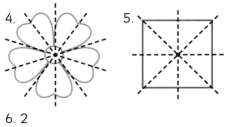   5.

6. 2
7. 2
8. 1

Practice questions

1.    2. b

Listening questions

These are the questions for the listening exercises on pages 24–25.

Read these questions aloud, as your child writes the answers on pages 24–25.
Copy the questions or take a quick photo to read from, so that your child can work in the book uninterrupted.

Before you read the questions, make sure your child is concentrating and that they know where they are meant to be writing their answers. Read each question twice, leaving a short gap in-between. You can emphasise the underlined words. Allow enough time for your child to write their answer before moving on to the next question.

1. Circle the largest number.

2. Circle the shape that has <u>half</u> shaded.

3. Circle the number that is <u>half</u> of <u>12</u>.

4. What number is halfway between <u>62</u> and <u>70</u>?

5. Look at the bicycles. Each bicycle has <u>two</u> wheels.
How many wheels are there on <u>four</u> bicycles?

Practice questions

1. Look at the pattern.
Write the missing number.

2. Look at the dice.
What number do you get when all the dots are added together?

3. Circle the answer to the following question.
What is <u>10</u> × <u>3</u>?